ORSON'S FARM™
GOES HALF HOG! 2

JIM DAVIS

ℛℛ
RAVETTE BOOKS

This edition first published by Ravette Books Limited 1988

Printed and bound in Great Britain
for Ravette Books Limited,
3 Glenside Estate, Star Road, Partridge Green,
Horsham, Sussex RH13 8RA
by Cox & Wyman Ltd, Reading

ISBN 1 85304 074 6

THERE'S GOTTA BE A WAY TO GET THAT APPLE

© 1986 United Feature Syndicate Inc

WAPE? JUST WHY ARE YOU DISGUISED AS A BUSH?

BECAUSE **THEY** MIGHT GET ME AND EAT ME

I'M SURE IF I WERE "**THEY**", THE FIRST PLACE I WOULD LOOK FOR LUNCH WOULD BE IN A BUSH

DISGUISED AS A BUSH. I DON'T BELIEVE IT

© 1986 United Feature Syndicate, Inc.

NOW A BALE OF HAY, THIS IS A NIFTY DISGUISE

JIM DAVIS 8-14

JIM DAVIS 8-29

© 1986 United Feature Syndicate, Inc

Other JIM DAVIS books published by Ravette

In this series

Goes half Hog! 1	£1.95
Counts Its Chickens 1	£1.95
Counts Its Chickens 2	£1.95
Rules The Roost 1	£1.95
Rules The Roost 2	£1.95

Garfield Pocket books

No. 1	Garfield The Great Lover	£1.95
No. 2	Garfield Why Do You Hate Mondays?	£1.95
No. 3	Garfield Does Pooky Need You?	£1.95
No. 4	Garfield Admit It, Odie's OK!	£1.95
No. 5	Garfield Two's Company	£1.95
No. 6	Garfield What's Cooking?	£1.95
No. 7	Garfield Who's Talking?	£1.95
No. 8	Garfield Strikes Again	£1.95
No. 9	Garfield Here's Looking At You	£1.95
No. 10	Garfield We Love You Too	£1.95
No. 11	Garfield Here We Go Again	£1.95
No. 12	Garfield Life and Lasagne	£1.95
No. 13	Garfield In The Pink	£1.95
No. 14	Garfield Just Good Friends	£1.95
No. 15	Garfield Plays It Again	£1.95
No. 16	Garfield Flying High	£1.95

All these books are available at your local bookshop or news-agent, or can be ordered direct from the publisher. Just tick the titles you require and fill in the form below. Prices and availability subject to change without notice. A full list of our publications is available. Please send your request to the address below.

Ravette Books Limited, 3 Glenside Estate, Star Road, Partridge Green, Horsham, West Sussex RH13 8RA

Please send a cheque or postal order, and allow the following for postage and packing. UK: 45p for one book plus 20p for the second book and 15p for each additional book.

Name ....

Address ....

....